To: _____

From: _____

Published by InnerSources, Inc.
the good messages company
329 10th Avenue SE
Cedar Rapids, Iowa 52401

First edition: April 2004

ISBN:1-883794-42-0

Other books by Terri Hoyland Wendler:
> *Heartlights*
> *Voyages*
> *Connections*
> *Celebrations of the Heart*
> *Tapping the Human Spirit*
> *I have CANcer: A Workbook/Journal for Those Diagnosed with Cancer*

Wise Words: Inspirational Thoughts is a series of books written to touch the hearts of those dealing with critical issues by offering them hope and courage.

Wise Words: Inspirational Thoughts for Caregivers of the Seriously Ill
Wise Words: Inspirational Thoughts for Those Diagnosed with Breast Cancer
> Available September 1, 2004
Wise Words: Inspirational Thoughts for Those with Chronic Illness
> Available January 1, 2005
Wise Words: Inspirational Thoughts for Those on the Diet Roller Coaster
> Available April 1, 2005
Wise Words: Inspirational Thoughts for Families Living with Autism
> Available October 1, 2005
Wise Words: Inspirational Thoughts for Families Living with Alzheimer's
> Available January 1, 2006

Printed in the United States of America

Wise Words

Inspirational Thoughts
For Those
Diagnosed
with Cancer

Terri Hoyland Wendler

Many thanks to the following people

for their time and commitment to this book.

*The 50+ survivors who shared their
personal thoughts for your benefit.
I promised you no last names.*

The following professionals:

*Jan Overland
Dr. Barbi Kaplan-Frenkel
Dr. Kenneth Whitham
Mary K. White, R.N.
Sue Rowbotham, R.N.
Shelly Evans, LBSW
Vicki Finkstein
Iowa Blood and Cancer Care
Nancy Jolliffe, R.D.
Denise Piper, R.N.
Dr. John VanderZee
Traci Kullmer, proofreader
Marcy Bader
Guy Wendler
Sue MacGregor*

earing the words,

"you have cancer"
immediately changes you and the way
you see your life. It becomes a life-threatening,
powerful force that can sometimes seem
to take over and control us - through fear.

We hope this book will help you reduce
the size and power of this force - and the
formidable word, CANCER - so that you
can fight and better survive this disease.

Who better to tell you what to expect than
those who have journeyed through the
cancer-ridden maze before you.

Read their wise words,
their favorite quotes, and
their ideas on how to cope
when all seems, at first,
overwhelming and downright scary.

Getting the Diagnosis

Oh, God, no!

"**P**erhaps

I am ***stronger***
than
I think."

Thomas Merton

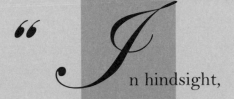

"*I*n hindsight,

hearing the diagnosis
that I had cancer was worse at the beginning.
All I could focus on was 'How am I going to
get through this?' Each day got easier to bear.
Each day I found I could think more clearly
when I lived one day at a time."

Sarah, 68

Sarah has been diagnosed with cancer twice and successfully completed treatment twice. Seven years later, she is still cancer free.

 ore than

1.2 million people will receive a diagnosis of cancer some time this year. The good news is that survival from some cancers has improved dramatically since the early 1970s. Skin cancers and testicular cancers, in particular, have excellent survival rates. Breast cancer, leukemia, and prostate cancer are showing improved survival rates. Strides are being made for gynecological system and colorectal cancers as well.

It is important to learn as much as you can about your particular type of cancer so you can make informed decisions about your health care.

Remember that statistics are just that: *statistics.*
And statistics do not take into account your personal characteristics:
other health factors
home environment
life enrichment
and
your ability to cope,
to name a few....

n addition,

more than 1 million others will be treated for localized (on the surface) skin cancers. Many of these may be easily removed if caught early. That is the key: early detection.

Anyone who finds a "mole" that seems to have popped up suddenly or changes in appearance (usually getting darker in color) should have it checked immediately. It is better to get an opinion that it is nothing to be concerned about rather than wonder.

Just like monthly breast exams are a good habit, so is visually checking your skin for unusual colorations and changes.

Another important preventative measure is wearing sunscreens, hats, and protective clothing. Don't forget that even in the winter, the sun can affect your skin.

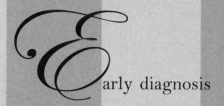arly diagnosis

and treatment are key to higher survival rates. Yearly mammograms, colorectal exams, and pap smears are but a few of the diagnostic tools available today.

We continue to study the links between genetics and the predisposition to certain cancers, and this research can help us identify high-risk individuals, thus making sure they are more carefully screened.

Research continues on drugs that may reduce the risk of cancer: Tamoxifen and Arimdex for breast cancer or Zolodex for prostate cancer.

Don't give up hope because tomorrow may produce the breakthrough needed for your specific type of cancer.

"*God,*

Grant me the **grace**
to accept with **serenity**
the things that cannot be changed;
Courage to change the things
that can be changed;
and the **wisdom**
to know the difference."

Reinhold Niebuhr

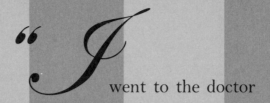

"*I* went to the doctor

because I found a lump and was told that day
that it was probably cancerous.

"I decided to get a **second opinion**
and thank God, I did. I didn't have
cancer at all. I'd tell every one to get a second
opinion. Your doctor shouldn't be threatened if
he or she is truly concerned about your
welfare. Learning everything possible is in
your best interest."

Linda, 38

*Linda learned the initial diagnosis was incorrect
after several more tests. She is healthy today
with no signs of cancer. She advises us to get
second opinions AND regular check-ups.*

"*I* found a mole

on my face. When I was having an annual check-up, I had my doctor examine the area. He told me it was nothing to be worried about. It kept getting a little bit bigger. My husband kept asking me to get another opinion and I told him it was nothing.

"After several months, my husband finally made an appointment for me with another physician. This doctor diagnosed a melanoma. I had it surgically removed. I then had to go through reconstructive surgery around the affected area.

"Thank God for my husband's persistance."

Sue, 60

Don't ignore any changes in or on your body. Sue says you know your body better than any doctor so pay attention to it.

*G*athering information

is important to the newly diagnosed patient so he
or she can make informed decisions.

Local Professional Sources:
your doctor and staff

American Cancer Society:
(local chapters in most areas)

Web sites:
www.cancer.org
American Cancer Society tracks statistics and survival rates
www.cancure.org
Information on alternative/integrative therapies
www.cancerfatigue.org
Information on the exhaustion that often follows therapy
www.cancer.gov
Newest clinical studies
www.leukemia-lymphoma.org
Information on all blood related diseases
www.cancerrd.com
*Latest nutritional information; a good place to
post your nutritional questions*

Magazines:
Cure
For a free subscription,
call 1-800-210-CURE (2873)
Coping
Subscription $19 6 issues/yr
1-615-790-2440

Books:

American Cancer Society, *Pain Control: A Guide for People with Cancer and Their Families*

Conner, Kristine and Lauren Langford, *Ovarian Cancer: A Guide for Women and Those Who Care About Them,* May 2003

Dollinger, Malin, M.D and Ernest Rosenbaum M.D. with Margaret Tempera, *Everyone's Guide to Cancer Therapy, 4th Edition*, December 2002

Gordon, James S., and Sharon Curtin, *"Comprehensive Cancer Care: Integrating Alternative, Complementary and Conventional Therapies,"* June 2000

Henschke, Claudia, Sarah Wernick and Peggy McCarthy, *"Lung Cancer: Myths, Facts, Choices... and Hope"*, October 2003

Hoyland, Terri, *"I have CANcer: A Workbook/Journal for the Person Diagnosed with Cancer,"* InnerSources Inc., 2001

Lerner, Michael, *"Choices in Healing: Integrating the Best of Conventional and Complementary Approaches to Cancer"*, 1996

National Institute of Health, *Nutrition for the Person with Cancer: A Guide for Patients and Families*

Quillin, Patrick with Noreen Quillin, *Beating Cancer with Nutrition: Combining the Best of Medicine and Nature for Full Spectrum Healing in the 21st Century*, January 2001

Walsh, Patrick and Janet Farrar Worthington, *Dr. Patrick Walsh's Guide to Surviving Prostate Cancer*, August 2002

"Trust me when I say

that the first few days after being told
I had cancer were the worse. It does get better.
Every fear and bad thought I could have, I had.
I felt devastated.
I felt helpless.
I felt like giving up.
I was paralyzed from thinking anything other
than the worst. And then over time, I
began to pull all my inner strength together
and decided to fight. Yes, there were moments
when I still felt afraid but I found
deep reservoirs of strength and resolve
I didn't know I had."

Mary, 68

*Mary was initially diagnosed with breast cancer seven
years ago. At first, she refused to talk about it, sitting for
long periods by herself. Her family felt isolated and left out,
but Mary says she needed time to come to terms with her
illness. She says she is very private by nature
and never spent lots of time talking about her feelings.*

 **"I** wanted to talk

to my mom about her feelings–and mine–
but her desire <u>NOT TO</u> share won out.
I had to find others to talk with: my sister,
my brother, friends. We realized that we
needed to respect her wishes even if
we didn't understand them. I did understand
that Mom needed to be in charge
of her own recovery."

Stuart. 44

*Stuart advises family members to take their lead from
the patient–even if you don't like or understand it.*

hen picking

a physician or treatment center, there are several things to consider besides whether or not you connect with the doctor:

Ask if there is a **Nurse Educator** on staff. A Nurse Educator is someone who is dedicated to answering your questions and researching your needs. Many offices now offer such support services.

Ask if there is a **Registered Dietitian.** Nutrition is important for overall health and healing. Helping cancer patients deal with their specific nutritional issues is becoming recognized as an important component.

Ask if there is a **Financial Counselor**. Handling insurance and understanding your insurance coverage and financial responsibilities can be overwhelming.

Ask about a **patient-centered philosophy:** one that incorporates and encourages alternative and complimentary care including music, art, imagery, and massage therapy.

Also, if you work, finding **treatment centers that will accommodate your work schedule** is imperative. Ask if they provide service only during the usual work hours of 8 a.m. to 5 p.m. or if they open early or stay open past 5 p.m.

"Become willing

to see the **hand of God**

and **accept** it
as a **friend's** offer
to **help** you with
what you are doing."

Julia Cameron

"Faced with a crisis,

the man of **character**

falls back

on **himself.**"

Charles de Gaulle

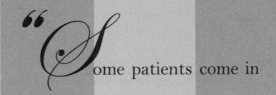**"S**ome patients come in

asking how long do they have.
I'd advise them ***NOT TO ASK!***
There are lots of people who have been told a
time limit and it became a self-fulfilling prophesy.
They died according to what they were told.

"However, there are many others who have
lived well beyond those time limits. Some of
them have even defied great odds and lived
many years beyond and a few have
recovered completely.

"If you are susceptible to suggestion, remember
that time limits are **just an opinion** and that
it doesn't take into account your will to live and
other unmeasurable factors.

"Medicine is making **significant** advances
each and every year. We don't know what new
discovery and treatment might be available
next year-or next month. Don't give up
because of your fears. Decide to fight for
your life until you are no longer
afraid to let go of your life."

Sue Rowbotham, R.N., OCN

" know God will not give
me anything
I can't handle.

I just wish He didn't
trust me so much."

Mother Teresa

 study

by the **National Institute of Health**
concluded that 40% of all cancer patients
suffer from malnutrition.

So...
when you have an appetite,
try to eat as many servings of
fruits and vegetables
as you can manage.

**Learn as much as you can about nutrition
so it can work in your body's favor.**

Afterall, your body is your temple.

"*Make* your

own **recovery**

the first **priority**

of your life."

Robin Norwood

"*I* was always so able to

handle so many roles; mom, wife, caregiver, working professional. When I found I had cancer, I realized that I had to focus on caring for me. It didn't mean I loved others less. It's just that I couldn't do everything I did before. I needed my family to understand. I needed to let go of the guilt. I needed to let go of being super woman."

Joy, 60

Joy says balancing all the roles in her life was difficult but she learned to let go of some of those expectations. Joy says that maintaining those high expectations was probably more in her head than truly expected by others.

"It seemed

like a roller coaster ride from day to day.
The tumor was small and caught early, then I
was waiting to hear if the lymph nodes were
involved. One day it was just surgery, the
next, radiation and chemotherapy.

"I survived by listening to that day's information,
then going home and researching it through the
internet or discussing things with friends. They
gave me questions to ask, and I heard story after
story of people who were living long
after their bout with cancer ended."

Robin, 55

*Seek all the information you need, says Robin. For
instance, she learned about sentinel node biopsy from a
friend and, armed with that knowledge, she was able to
eliminate one surgical procedure originally recommended
by her doctor.*

"You can do

what you have to do,

and some times you can do it
even better
than you think you can."

President Jimmy Carter

"*R*emember that the most important person on your health care team is you. You are the captain. It is not the surgeon or even the oncologist. It is you. It is your illness and it is in your body. You are the one who knows what is best for you. Don't let anyone railroad you into doing anything you aren't comfortable doing. Ask questions and keep on asking until any doubts or concerns you have are gone."

Tasha, 62

Tasha was treated for breast cancer several years ago. She says that one of the "gifts" she received from this illness is that she became more assertive.

"*I* stopped letting people take advantage of me. I started asking for what I wanted and I found that life was a whole lot more fun."

"*I* encourage

my patients to have *faith* in God,

but not to expect God

to do all the work."

Dr. Bernie Siegel, M.D.

"I think

controlling your attitude is the key to healing more rapidly. I just kept telling myself that worrying about having cancer wasn't going to help. I compared it to playing golf. When I worry about my shot, it's not usually as good as when I swing thinking I'm going to have a good shot. So I concentrated on thinking I was going to get better."

George, 55

To help manage the worry, George says to stay busy so you don't have time to sit around and let cancer consume your thoughts. He also says this is the time to treat yourself well so schedule something fun every day and break the usual routines.

 lways leave

enough time in your life
to do something
that makes you
happy,
satisfied,
even **joyous**.

That has more of an effect
on ***well-being***
than any other single factor."

Paul Hawken

"**I** can

be **changed**
by what happens to me.

But I **refuse**
to be reduced by it."

Maya Angelou
Poet/Author

"Rationally, I knew I had had a long and relatively healthy 75 years. I was thankful for my family and my many blessings, but I prayed to God for more years, more wonderful life. I thought, "Just because I'm old, please don't give up on me." I am certain that I have the strength to face whatever God has planned. I made it through the horrors of World War II, but there is more I want to experience."

Doug, 75

Doug underwent hormone therapy followed by a radiation seed implant. So far, his prognosis looks good. Don't feel guilty for wanting to live, Doug advises.

 here are

two ways
to approach *life-*

as a victim

or as a *fighter.*"

Merle Shain

Going Through Treatment

The Healing Process

"There are so many things to think about when it comes to getting treatment, and they all have a role. There are the traditional methods: chemotherapy, surgery, medication, and radiation. And there are all kinds of non-traditional aspects as well: nutrition, touch therapies, music therapies, naturopathy, mind-body medicine, and even spiritual support. I chose to use a combination of these treatments. Not all of my friends and family agreed on what they thought I should do, but I decided to listen to my heart. I may never know what truly made the difference, but it doesn't matter. The fact is, I got better."

Martha, 58

Martha says she had a radical mastectomy as well as chemotherapy and radiation. She also changed her diet significantly, practiced visualization, and attended a support group for breast cancer survivors. Martha has been cancer-free for six years.

"*I*t's only when

we **truly** know and understand
that we have
a **limited time** on earth–
and that we have no way
of knowing when our time is up–
that we will **begin to live**
each day to the **fullest,**
as if it was the **only one** we had."

Elisabeth Kubler-Ross
Author

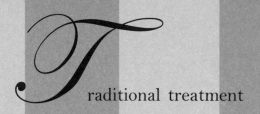 raditional treatment

usually includes one or a combination of
the following modalities

Surgery: removal of the tumor by
operating on it
This is the most common treatment

Radiation: treatment of the disease with high
energy x-rays directly to the area
About 50% undergo radiation

Chemotherapy: the use of cytotoxic
chemicals to systemically treat the
disease given intravenously or orally

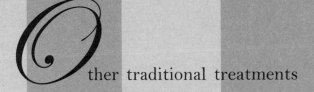ther traditional treatments

may include the following modalities

Hormonal: employs or manipulates bodily hormones

Immunotherapy: enhances the body's own immune function

Investigative: clinical research trials

Targeted Therapies: treatments that actually are directed to the human cells themselves

*T*hings to know about radiation therapy:

Radiation is not painful. The machine that goes around you is open and doesn't touch you while precisely treating the involved region. Some patients describe a slight warming or tingling of the skin.

Over time, your skin may become dry, itchy and irritated. However, the day-to-day treatment is not uncomfortable.

External radiation will not make you radio active at any time. The few patients that receive internal radiation may be isolated immediately following the procedure or instructed on necessary safety precautions.

Radiation will cause hair loss ONLY if the area being treated is your head. Most patients find that their hair grows back after treatments are finished.

Radiation to varying sites may cause different side effects. The most common are fatigue and skin changes. Ask your doctor or nurse what you should expect. If you have questions or concerns, you should be able to discuss them with any member of the team of professionals involved in your care including, your doctor, medical physicist, or nurse. You should be encouraged to actively participate in your treatment.

"Difficult times

have helped me
to understand better than before
how **infinitely rich**
and **beautiful**
life is
in **every** way,
and that so many things
that one goes about
worrying about
are of **no importance**
whatsoever."

Isak Dinesen

"Stay with

traditional treatment and enhance them with non-traditional therapies. In my work, I see that people do better-have fewer side effects, stay more active, and experience less depression-when they incorporate non-traditional therapies with their treatments. I especially notice that those who follow their own spiritual or religious beliefs and incorporate them into their treatments seem to do better. I can't put my finger on why except that these spiritual practices provide more hope to a patient and that hope improves their quality of life.

"So don't pooh-pooh any therapies that are not grounded in traditional medicine if you want to try them. Anything that makes you feel better probably works on some level."

Sue Rowbotham, R.N., OCN

" Affirmations

are like **prescriptions**

for **certain aspects**

of yourself

you want to **change.**"

Jerry Frankhauser

*F*illing our minds with positive thoughts

or affirmations may help us face difficult situations. There are many nationally known proponents who believe that positive thoughts help us fight illness:

Dr. Bernie Siegel
Dr. Joan Borysenko
Shakti Gawain
Dr. Deepak Chopra
Dr. Wayne Dyer
Helen Hay

These are just a few of the professionals who
believe that one's mind can influence the
ability to fight illness.
If they help us get well, great.
If they give us strength to cope, that's fine too.

Following are examples of some
positive affirmations:

*Deep within me is an enormous wellspring of
strength I can tap into when I need it.*

*I am capable of facing difficult times with
fortitude, courage, and calmness.*

Hope is my legacy and I intend to fully feel it today.

*I am in charge of my treatment and
I intend to face it courageously.*

With the help of God, I will get through this crisis.

I am capable of deciding what I should do.

*For today, I let go of my need to control every outcome,
and I put my health in God's hands.*

*I allow myself to accept help and support from others
because I deserve to be loved and cared for.*

Life is my gift and I intend to live it fully.

*I have more strength and courage than I imagined.
It never runs dry.*

Think of affirmations that help you feel
strong, capable, and resourceful.

Write them here:

_____

_____

_____

_____

_____

_____

"The world

is round
and the place
which may **seem** like the end
may also be only . . .

the beginning."

Ivy Baker Priest

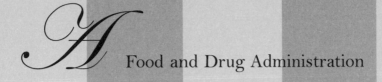 Food and Drug Administration

study
estimated that **40%** of those diagnosed with cancer also pursued non-traditional treatments.

Some of those treatments include:

music therapy
diet and nutrition
massage and touch therapies
visualization and positive affirmations
support groups
spiritual healing
religious rituals
acupuncture
holistic approaches like
black cohosh or flax seed***
meditation and prayer

*** Check on the latest results because there
may be controversy over different
holistic approaches.

acing surgery

is hard. You wonder what they will find when
they open you up. Is the cancer contained or will
they find it is far worse than they thought?
What if they don't get it all? What if there is a
reaction to the anesthetic? What if I just don't
survive? I'd certainly heard the worst case
scenarios and prayed I wouldn't be one of them.
And I wasn't.

"Then I worried about how quickly I'd heal, how
soon I could get back to normal. And that too
passed. I did return to normal. I did get
my life back and in time, I even forgot how
scared and worried I had been."

Robert, 72

*Robert recognized that he had to put his life,
certainly his outcome, in the hands of a surgeon he
barely knew. Research their credentials. Get
recommendations. Talk to other patients about
their experiences. And remember that your case is not
the same as anyone else's. Balance all these opinions.*

"**N**ights sometimes

seemed racked with wide-awake nightmares. My body wasn't busy so my mind had plenty of time to wander, and it sure did wander. The worst-case scenarios played over and over again in my head.

"To get through the night, I played soothing music, exercised so hard that I was exhausted, and sometimes listened to books on tape to help me fall asleep. I also used relaxation techniques like progressive muscle relaxation and gentle breathing exercises. My doctor put me on an anti-anxiety medication for a while, which also helped.

"Don't let the night time get to you. Make your mind tune in to happy things like a dream trip or plan a fun event like a birthday celebration. If you need to, ask your doctor for suggestions on how to handle your anxiety."

Jane, 64

Jane went through surgery, radiation, and chemotherapy. She had lymph node involvement and had to wait many months to see if she responded to treatment. She has so far....

"Take advantage of

the registered dietitian in your cancer center. First of all, good nutrition provides you with energy and the building blocks your body needs to function properly and stay in good repair.

"Good nutrition is even more necessary when you have cancer. During treatment, good nutrition can help you to feel better, keeping up your strength and energy, as well as maintaining your weight and nutrition stores. In addition, good nutrition boosts your immune system by decreasing your risk of infection and helps you heal and recover quickly.

"Generally speaking, taking a multivitamin/ mineral supplement is a good thing if one cannot get nutrients from real food. But talk to your health care provider before continuing to take them during treatment.

"Many patients with a cancer diagnosis find their intake diminishes due to the treatment related side effects. One solution is eating smaller, more frequent meals utilizing high calorie/high protein items. Your dietitian will assist you in identifying nutrient-dense foods/fluids that will be tolerated in these small frequent feedings. "

Nancy Jolliffe, R.D., L.D
Registered Dietitian

"When I

started treatment, including radiation
and chemotherapy, the idea of six months to a
year to complete treatment seemed too
overwhelming. When I decided to look at it
one day at a time, it became more managable.

"If I felt sick one day, I could say to myself,
'That's one day. Tomorrow will be different.' It
was easier than thinking, 'I could have a year
of this?' I found that living one day at a time
gave me a clean slate every day."

Ruth Ann, 68

*Focusing on one day at a time gave Ruth Ann
permission to let go of the bad times. Each day
she started over again. Ruth Ann says she has
adopted that attitude today and it helps her to
live today more joyously.*

"When I was diagnosed with esophageal cancer, my doctor gave me a very poor prognosis. I decided I would seek a second opinion because I was not ready to accept his outlook. I made it clear that I wanted someone who would fight for me. My new doctor did just that.

"I went through an intensive combination chemotherapy-radiation treatment and when that was completed, I then underwent surgery to remove my esophagus and reconstruct it. The surgery was done robotically and lasted 13 hours. It took me a long time to regain my strength.

"My prognosis today? Great! My check-ups have all been cancer-free. I'm feeling good. I'm feeling so good that I'm ready to go back to work full-time."

Karen, 52

Karen did not settle for the first prognosis she was given and says don't you settle either. She endured several months of constant sickness during her intensive treatment. Even during the worst times, she told herself she was not giving up. She says don't you give up either.

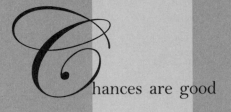 hances are good

that you will experience some side effects if you go through chemotherapy or radiation. What side effects one may experience will vary from person to person, and treatment to treatment. For example, some chemotherapy treatments result in hair loss and some don't. Your health care provider should give you more specific information as you review your treatment options.

Generally, the most commonly reported side effects are nausea and fatigue along with hair loss and loss of appetite. Others report pain, queasiness, vomiting, diarrhea, constipation, sleeplessness, sore or irritated throat, or dry mouth. Some say they experience anxiety and depression as well.

Consequently, it is impossible to predict what side effects any one person may experience. Therefore, when you experience a change in your health, tell your health care professionals about it. Don't ignore it or hope it goes away. There are ways to relieve many of these side effects.

Sue Rowbotham, R.N., OCN

 expected

to experience side effects. All the health care providers told me that there were side effects and that I would probably experience some. They gave me booklets and pages of information to read. I read through them all and believed I was ready.

"I suffered from night sweats and sleeplessness and that was not one of the side effects I had information on. Then I wondered if something else was wrong. I suffered through sleepless nights for three weeks before I brought it up to my doctor. She told me it was related to fatigue and gave me medication to help me sleep. The symptoms subsided.

"I learned that side effects don't fit neatly into categories so trust your instincts. If something seems out-of-sync, pay attention to it. Don't let it go because you don't want to be a bother. You know your body better than anyone else. Listen to it."

Joy, 60

As a volunteer in a cancer hospital, Joy helps patients understand what is happening to them. She says every person is different. Their experience is different. Health care providers can sometimes forget about our uniqueness because they are dealing with so many patients at one time. Joy says we must be our own best advocate.

"**W**hen you're lonely,

I wish you **love.**
When you're down,
I wish you **joy**.
When you're troubled,
I wish you **peace.**
When things are complicated,
I wish you **simple beauty.**
When things are chaotic,
I wish you **inner silence.**
And when things look empty,
I wish you **hope.**

Unknown

*This message was given to survivor, Kathy, by a
good friend when Kathy was recovering from
cancer. That was more than 10 years ago. She
keeps it on her mirror because it brought her a
sense of comfort. She wanted to share it with
you, hoping it will bring you comfort, too.*

"**G**rant that

I may become **beautiful**
in my **soul** within,

and that all my external possessions
may be in **harmony**
with my **inner self**."

Adapted from a speech by Plato

*H*air loss may be a side effect from

certain chemotherapies. Ask your health care professionals if this might happen to you. Here are some suggestions to help you emotionally and physically cope with that possibility:

Most communities today have one or more salons that specialize in helping cancer patients with hair loss: special cuts, wig fittings, and hairpieces.

To find out who specializes in this area, ask at your oncologist's office for a recommendation.

If you go to the phone book, look under **wigs** in the business pages. The salons that specialize in serving cancer patients will state this information in their ads.

Several patients have said that it helps to go and pick out a wig before you begin to lose your hair. That way you've already seen yourself in this new hair style. Also, you can have it styled the way you want and it won't be such a shock later.

"*I*t was

incredibly hard to lose my breast after a mastectomy but it was easy to hide. When I walked down the street, no one could tell at a glance that I had only one breast because the prothesis looked so natural. However, it was worse losing my hair. I guess because it was so obvious that something was "wrong." Hair is our crowning glory and I'd lost mine."

Carol, 72

Carol had a mastectomy at a time when it was the routine thing to do. Now a lumpectomy may be a viable choice. She advises others to make sure a mastectomy is absolutely necessary before agreeing to undergo surgery.

Carol also went through chemotherapy as a preventative measure. That was 12 years ago and she's still getting clean check-ups.

"*I*'ve had lots of bad hair days throughout my life, but never appreciated them until I saw myself totally bald. I'd trade a day of being bald for a bad hair day anytime. Never again will I take my hair for granted."

Ginger, 46

Losing her hair was really tough. It happened sooner than they told her. Ginger thought she was emotionally ready to deal with it, but when her hair began to fall out, she was devastated. She would sob, then just sit there without moving and stare into space, then sob some more. It took Ginger weeks to adjust.

 bout 50%

of those patients who go through chemotherapy say they experience nausea. It is typically the most uncomfortable side effect. Nausea may or may not include vomiting.

Following are some suggestions to help alleviate nausea:

Eat dry foods such as crackers and toast. (Not for throat or neck cancers)

Eat smaller meals more often, around six smaller meals per day.

Fresh fruits help some patients. Others advise you to avoid high-fat foods.

Eat salty foods and avoid really sweet foods. One patient swore by tomato soup.

Drink gingerroot or chamomile tea and add peppermint.

Ask for prescription anti-nausea medication or Travel-Eze anti-nausea wristbands.

Try relaxation techniques such as meditation, yoga, and biofeedback.

Slowly drink clear, cool liquids such as iced green tea, gingerale, popsicles, or apple juice cubes.

Again, meet with the dietitian for more suggestions

"*I* like living.

I have sometimes been wildly,
despairingly,
acutely miserable,
racked with sorrow,
but through it all
I still knew quite certainly
that **just to be alive** is
a **grand thing**."

Agatha Christie
Author

"When we walk

to the **edge**
of all the light we have
and take a **step** into
the **darkness** of the **unknown**,
we must believe one of
two things will happen-

there will be something
solid for us to **stand** upon,
or we **will** be taught to **fly**."

Anonymous

"My doctor

told me that healthy people tended to heal
faster than unhealthy people, so I immediately
adopted healthier habits. I gave up alcohol,
caffeine, fatty foods, and desserts. I began walking
every day to build stamina. I began to take
vitamins. I watched my stress levels
by not working such long days and scheduling
fun activities. I prepared a list of the
blessings in my life.

"I came through surgery and felt relatively good
in a day or two. I attribute part of it to
my improved health profile. Why I didn't do
these things all along, I just don't know"

George, 55

*A corporate executive, George dined out a lot and
often worked into the evening. He has set a goal to
be the first in his family to live to be 100 years old-
and having had cancer is not going to change his goal.*

 visualization technique

that sees your body effectively fighting cancer cells involves:

1. *Picture your cancer cells as weak, slow, and docile (rather than powerful and dominating).*

2. *Imagine scenes where your treatment is "fighting" these cancer cells.*

3. *Imagine your body fighting these cancer cells.*

4. *Visualize your body conquering the weak cells and building a strong immune system that is overcoming the cancer.*

5. *See the cancer cells shrinking slowly away until they totally disappear.*

6. *See yourself victorious over the cancer. See yourself filled with good health, energy, and strength.*

 **y biggest fear was**

that I would come through treatment and find I was impotent. For a man, that was a big deal. It haunted me. I finally decided to talk to my doctor about my fears, and he was very reassuring. He didn't say it wasn't a possibility, but he gave me a realistic expectation. That helped.

"My wife was great. She reassured me over and over again that she still loved me and that she wouldn't ever stop loving me."

Robert, 67

Robert says he is thankful for his wife's attitude and stability. She let him take things at his pace and reassured him when his body wasn't fully functioning. He says their sex life has returned.

"The body

must be **nourished**
physically,
emotionally,
and **spiritually.**

We're spiritually **starved** in
this culture–
not underfed
but undernourished.

Carol Horning

" *I* n my work with

cancer patients, I've noticed that many of them experience depression. I now advise those just receiving a cancer diagnosis to expect that they will experience depression. I think it is more the norm than not. If and when you feel depressed, discuss it with your physician. He or she can help you cope with this side of the illness through medication, counseling, and/or getting you into a support group.

"Our patients who participate in support groups tend to find depression subsides when they can talk about their illness and realize that they aren't alone. I've become a real advocate for support groups "

Sue Rowbotham, R.N., OCN

"**S**omeone **dear**

is one

to whom we can **pour** out
all the contents of our heart,
chaff and grain together,
knowing that the gentlest hands
will take and **sift** it,
keep what's worth keeping and
with the breath of **kindness**,
blow the rest **away.**"

Arabian Proverb

$\mathcal{B}$e aware

that you may qualify for a temporary seat belt exemption when undergoing radiation therapy, so you do not need to wear your shoulder belt when you are in the car. This is especially important for patients with breast, neck, or throat cancers.

Some people may experience skin irritation during radiation therapy, and seat belts can rub against the area. Protect yourself by learning about this exemption.

Ask at your doctor's office for more information.

Advice from Jan Overland
Office Administrator

 lot of patients

find that while they are receiving or undergoing chemotherapy or radiation treatments, their appetite diminishes. One way we encourage our patients to eat is to work on 'plate presentation' so they want to eat what is in front of them. We make sure that the food looks appealing on the plate. We use food that is both colorful and nutritious: several types of melons or grapes with small portions of meat and chopped broccoli along with a glass of apple juice, for example. That way they have a variety of healthy choices that are good for them.

"So, when the plate is set down in front of the patient, he or she actually eats more because it looks good. It does work, so try it when a person's appetite is particularly minimal."

Donna Smith
Registered Dietitian

"*L*et your **dreams,**

not your regrets,

take **command**

of your life."

Rev. Robert Schuller

 found myself

not able to get moving. I would sit on the couch
for hours not really feeling anything. I had no
energy and stopped caring. My wife would
cajole me, tease me, yell at me, and ignore me. I
was so depressed that I just didn't care. I didn't
understand how much chemo wiped me out.
I got better once treatments ended. I wish
someone had taken the time to explain how
draining chemo could be."

Daniel, 62

*Daniel says no one can know how much energy
chemotherapy treatments take out of you.
He is back on his feet working part-time as a
handyman. And 10 years later, he is still cancer-free.*

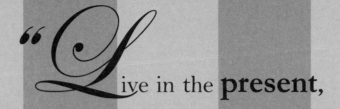

"Live in the **present,**

do **all** the things
that **need to be done,**

do **all** the **good**
you can each day,

the **future** will unfold."

Peace Pilgrim

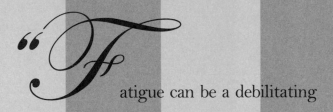

"**F**atigue can be a debilitating

side effect for many patients undergoing radiation or chemotherapy. It is often overlooked or minimized by health care providers and their patients. As fatigue may have many causes, there may be several methods to lessen its effects.

"Please tell your health care professionals so they can help you."

Mary K. White, R.N.
Oncology Certified Nurse

"While I was going through chemotherapy and radiation, I found I was getting extremely tired during the day. I had to work. I had to earn a paycheck. So, I asked my boss if I could bring in a recliner chair and put it in the back room. She was very supportive and said, 'Of course.'

"When I found myself tired, I would lie down in the recliner for maybe 15 minutes, sometimes 30 minutes. It helped me get through the day. Then I could get back to work and be more productive again.

"It was a win-win situation for me and for my employer. This way, I didn't have to take time off work and they found I could continue getting my work done."

Robin, 55

Work with your employer, says Robin. She understands that the workplace has to continue to operate and Robin wants to continue to do a good job. Hopefully, your employer will be accommodating at a time like this when he or she understands what you are going through and that you are trying to remain a hard working dedicated employee.

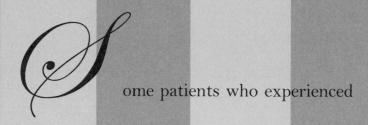

ome patients who experienced

chronic fatigue gave the
following suggestions:

Reduce stress. Say 'No.' Delegate. Meditate, Pray. Read. Listen to music. Practice deep breathing.

Today there are some medications that may help control fatigue. Ask your doctor if you are experiencing this side effect.

Balance rest and activities. Shorter rest periods are reported to be better than one long one.

Eat a balanced diet when you can. Some survivors swore by eating smaller meals. One said her mainstay was tomato soup. Another said peppermint or chamomile tea helped her. Ask your dietitian for more suggestions.

It is also shown that people who are even moderately active (walk, do yoga or exercises, garden, golf) experience less fatigue than those who do absolutely no exercise. Ask your doctor for a fitness plan.

This fatigue is very real. Remember that your body is using more energy to handle the demands of cancer and treatment.

ake time to learn

about the different treatments and research studies. Several friends told me about treatments that had worked for them or someone they knew. Oftentimes these were things my doctor had not mentioned to me. I would go to the Internet and learn about them. If it seemed like a possibility, I then asked my doctor about it. We would have a discussion about whether or not he thought it was feasible for me and all the reasons why. It built my confidence in what we were doing when I understood the treatment approaches and why they may or may not work for me.

"After I finished chemotherapy and radiation, I then went into a research study. I did my own Internet research on the study before I decided to participate or not. I felt like I was more in control of what was going on when I could do my own research."

Margaret, 68

The Internet can be a valuable resource and Margaret says use it. She is glad to be a part of clinical studies and urges others to learn about all these options as well.

ost thou

love life?

Then **don't squander** time,
for that
is the stuff
life is made of."

Benjamin Franklin

"My boyfriend and

my parents never got along very well, but it became very obvious when we all had to spend so much time together in close quarters going to and from treatments and doctor's appointments. I was on edge wondering whose feelings were going to be upset next. I wanted to shout, 'Please, for my sake, leave your grudges at the door.'"

Barbara, 29

Barbara says her parents never thought her boyfriend was good enough for her and to her. She admits that when she became ill, she wondered if he would stick with her. She was pleasantly surprised to find he not only had staying power, but lots of compassion and understanding. Barbara wishes that her parents would give him a chance, but accepts that it doesn't look likely. However, Barbara feels much more secure in their relationship than before. That is a surpise gift she loves.

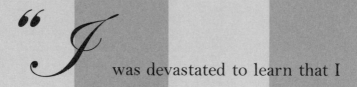

"*I* was devastated to learn that I didn't qualify for any clinical study. I wanted this so much that I did all the research on what was available. I also made calls to regional cancer centers but I learned that I didn't meet their stringent guidelines.

"I thought that participation in a study brought with it a guarantee for getting well and staying well. I was afraid I was getting a death sentence when I didn't qualify. However, I have been getting my check-ups for five years and have not had a recurrence. So, if someone doesn't qualify for a clinical study, don't give up hope."

Thomas, 62

Pursue learning about any kind of treatment that you become aware of. No one will fight for your health like you will. Don't wait for your doctor to bring it up, Thomas advises. Be proactive and ask your doctor to explore every possibility for you.

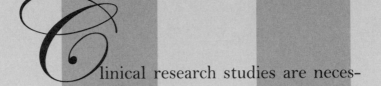linical research studies are neces-

sary if we are ever going to find better treatments and even cures for various cancers. If you
want to gather more information on how to
qualify, ask your health care professionals what
may be available, read *Coping* or *Cure* magazines,
or go on-line to ***www.cancer.gov***.

WARNINGS:

Be aware that clinical protocols tend to have very
specific criterion and not everyone will actually
qualify to participate.

Participation does not bring with it a guarantee of
a cure or even improved health. It is a <u>study</u> of
effects and changes.

"Perseverance is

a **great** element of **success.**
If you only
knock long enough
and **loud** enough
at the gate,
you are **sure** to **wake up** somebody."

Henry Wadsworth Longfellow

"I was overwhelmed

by all the insurance and financial questions I had, and I felt totally abandoned. Here I was, sick and I couldn't figure out what treatments were covered by my insurance and what wasn't. I didn't know which forms I should file and which should be filed by the health care providers. I was concerned about any out-of-pocket expenses I might incur.

"I found I had to be rather assertive if I was going to get any answers to my questions. I had to get pushy at times and demand help and assistance from office personnel and my insurance carrier. I now know that most offices have staff who specialize in financial counseling. I strongly advise other cancer patients to meet with their health providers' financial counselors or insurance specialists BEFORE beginning any course of treatment. It is imperative to contact your insurance company and learn about your specific coverage. Become informed."

Michael, 73

Don't hesitate to ask for help and keep on asking for help until you feel comfortable with the answers. Mike says you're not the dumb one. Insurance companies can make it complicated. Mike wonders, is it on purpose?

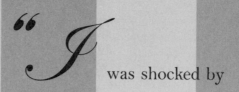 **"I** was shocked by

the number of people who reached out to me
after I learned I had cancer. I received notes and
cards from people I hardly knew. Lots of people
extended offers to help. I suppose I am a proud
person who hates to ask for help. At that time, I
was forced to accept help and learned that many
people genuinely want to help. So, my advice is:
LET THEM! I am a different person today
because I let people in. I am now more able to
express my true feelings. I am now more willing
to accept help and to reach out and help someone else in need. Hard to believe, but cancer
softened my attitude towards life. And life now
seems more satisfying."

Martha, 72

*Martha is a cancer survivor of 10 years. She is also
a survivor of other major life events like losing a
husband and a child. Her bout with cancer expanded
her circle of loved ones and mirrored her own inner
strength. When she suffered other losses, she found
internal and external resources she could tap into.*

oday, most

people who are undergoing chemotherapy and radiation continue to work. They continue to care for their families. They continue to live their regular lives.

"Part of it is because of advances in medicine: things like there are fewer side effects or they are less intense. Part of it is because we have learned how to deal with these side effects more effectively: foods that help nausea subside, for example, or scheduling routine naps.

"Today, there are more medications that help you keep going, restore your energy.

"Your medical staff can help you figure out how to keep going so you can continue your daily routine and take care of yourself so you can heal. Don't hesitate to discuss these things with your care providers."

Denise Player, R.N., OCN

 **"*M*y joy,**

my grief,

my hope,

my love,

did all within this circle move!"

Edmund Waller

Living

With

Cancer

Family, Friends, and Work

"**I**'ve become

very intolerant of people who complain a lot. When I listen to people whine about really trivial things like how their hair looks, that they can't afford a new stereo, or it took too long to get a meal, I think 'You idiot. Life is too precious and too wonderful.' Be grateful for what you've been given rather than what you don't have. You just don't know when it will be taken away from you."

Alison, 78

Alison has been cancer-free for 15 years.
Although it has been a long time,
she never forgets her experience with cancer.
She says she will never again take life for granted.
Allison is grateful for little things
and sees every day as a precious gift.

" *I* have

a lot of trouble with that expression, 'beating cancer'. I know people mean well when they say, 'You can beat this thing,' but it places an awfully heavy burden on those of us who already have enough to bear. I found that my faith in God got me through those tough times. I kept saying 'I place myself in Your Hands.'

Lois, 39

There are a lot of different philosophies about why one person gets cancer and why another person doesn't. Lois advises you not to listen to all those ideas. The important thing is to take care of yourself and live life according to your own rules. She is healthy today.

"Everyday living

requires **courage**.

We **must do** the things

we think we cannot do."

Eleanor Roosevelt

 was one
of those people who resented hearing people
say that cancer brought some kind of gift. I
thought, 'How can cancer ever be a blessing?'
It isn't. But now I see that the soul-searching
I did during that time changed the way I
lived. That was its own kind of gift."

Isabel, 52

*Isabel was cancer-free for four years before she
found out she was no longer in remission. She is
undergoing another round of chemotherapy. Isabel
is surrounded by family and friends who
adore and cherish her.*

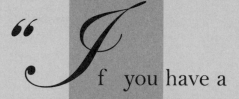

" *If* you have a

worry problem,
do these three things:

1. Ask yourself, 'What is the worst
   thing that can possibly happen?'

2. Prepare to accept it if you have to.

3. Then calmly prepare to improve
   upon the worst ."

Dale Carnegie

What Cancer Cannot Do

Cancer is so limited...
It cannot cripple **Love**
It cannot shatter **Hope**
It cannot corrode **Faith**
It cannot destroy **Peace**
It cannot kill **Friendship**
It cannot suppress **Memories**
It cannot invade the **Soul**
It cannot steal **Eternal Life**
It cannot conquer the **Spirit**

Unknown

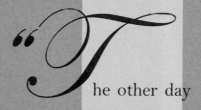

"The other day

my six year old hugged me so tightly, it's like I could feel his love invade my body and give me strength to go on fighting this disease. I clenched my jaw and thought, 'I'm not going to let this cancer get me.'"

Danielle, 28

Danielle's son is now 12 and she is gratefully watching him face his upcoming teenage years. Being loved and loving is a powerful reason to want to get well. Danielle held on to that thought when the going got tough. She believes in the power of positive thought.

"*W*hen dealing with

children, I suggest the following:
"Talk about it. Don't let them hear things from others. Children will imagine the worst if left out. Allow the child to process information in small bits. Give a child permission to ask questions. And talk about it again and again, if necessary.

"Address the issue of death up front. If your child goes to school, he or she has heard of someone dying of cancer and they will immediately project death on to you. Especially if the prognosis is excellent, bring it up so they don't secretly and needlessly worry. Reassure them that you are not dying.

"If the prognosis is more uncertain, you can say something like, "There is lots to be hopeful about. We'll get through this one day at a time."

"Remember that for kids and adults alike, sometimes 'mad' is easier that 'scared.' Don't let acting out behaviors get in the way of communication. And don't take it so personally.

"If you can, pair your child with an adult he or she can relate to. Arrange time alone with that person so they can talk. Oftentimes, your child will share fears with that adult because it is safer than with you.

"Many communities have programs for children with sick parents. Check them out to see if your child might benefit from one of them."

Shelly Evans, Social Worker

"My children

were in their teens when I was going through
treatment and recovery. And they weren't
very nice. They got upset when laundry
wasn't done or we were out of food. But
truthfully, I just couldn't keep up. And I felt
sorry for myself that they seemed so unaware
of what I was going through. My brother
stepped in and took them to lunch or to a
game. He listened to their thoughts, their
concerns, and he relayed my needs to them. He
didn't play at being a parent, but he was an
adult friend who mediated for both of us. It
really helped."

Virginia, 54

*Now that her children are adults, they realize how
tough this time was for their mom. Virginia says
you don't have to handle everything yourself.
Let other people in. It benefits* **_everyone._**

"**B**e willing

to have it be so.

Acceptance of
what has happened
is the **first** step
in **overcoming**
the consequences
of any misfortune."

William James

"Even adult children

are unpredictable. My daughter was dear and supportive. However, she wanted to mother me and I didn't want to be mothered. I just wanted her to be there. My son, on the other hand, was detached, not even calling after surgery to see how I fared.

"Don't be hurt by their reactions. I came to realize it has more to do with their personality types than whether or not they loved me.

"Non-family sources were actually more helpful than family because they aren't enmeshed in the family dynamics. They can just be there."

Sue, 60

Sue said it is important to have reasonable expectations for other people, especially family members. If you don't, you may find yourself hurt, angry, or frustrated because they don't act the way you'd like them to act.

 **y husband**

began to treat me like a fragile child. Yes, I was scared and uncertain but I needed more than ever before to feel like I was in control of something. At that time, I thought it was the treatment of my illness. I didn't want him to feel sorry for me or tell me what to do. I began to speak up more and say what I wanted."

Linda, 66

Linda had several frank discussions with her husband about her needs. She listened to what he also needed. It was his basic nature to take over and run the situation. Oftentimes in the past, she had let him. But in this situation, she felt she needed to be the one to decide what to do. Linda said their relationship became a stronger partnership and she became a stronger person.

A nother side benefit of being treated for cancer was my husband actually opened up more and shared more feelings. He learned that it was OK to express himself."

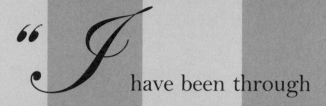

"*I* have been through

the depths of poverty and sickness.

When people ask me
what has kept me going
through the trouble
that comes to all of us,
I always reply,
'I stood yesterday.
I can stand today.
And I **will not** permit myself
to think about
what might happen tomorrow'"

Dorothy Dix.

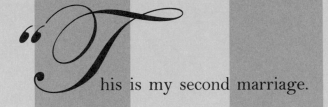

"This is my second marriage.

My husband has been so supportive of me as I've gone through this ordeal. And I thank God for him. He seemed to always know when I needed a shoulder and when I needed a push. It was interesting to me that his family was more caring than my own family.

"I'm not so sure my first husband would have been so understanding. He just wasn't as emotionally open and, frankly, just didn't seem to care about me the way John does.

"I realized that families are wonderful but I couldn't depend upon them for all my emotional needs. I still needed to find my own voice, my own strength."

Sue, 60

Sue says if you want her advice, don't depend too much upon your family. Every family member has his or her own issues, and it is hard to separate at times. Expect those issues to show up when you least expect-or need- them to. That way you'll still be able to cope with your own healing.

 o-do's that

will help strengthen your ability to fight disease and build wellness:

Drink eight glasses of water every day to keep yourself hydrated and your lymph system fluid.

Exercise. You only need to exercise until you feel an increase in your energy level. This isn't about running marathons. It's about increasing your energy levels.

Find things that make you laugh: Comics. Stories. Rent a funny movie. Go to a comedy club.

Plan some fun escapes: lunch with a special friend, walk in the park, sing, listen to music, take a drive.

Make a list of things you are grateful for.

 *was divorced*

when I first learned I had cancer. I certainly felt overwhelmed and very alone. It seemed so unfair that I was going to have to go through surgery and months of treatments all by myself.

"I was struck by the kindness of so many people who offered to help. A couple of them were close friends but many were only acquaintances. They offered to make meals, drive me places, or run errands for me. One person even offered to come over and help me clean from time to time.

"I will never forget these wonderful acts of kindness. I only hope that I can give back a little of that to someone else in need."

Jane, 68

Let people in. Jane says she was a private person who didn't like asking for help. She learned the joy of receiving support. It was truly a heartfelt gift.

"*W*hile I was battling

cancer, my faith in God was my foundation
of strength. In my weakest moments, I
believed God was holding me in the palm
of His hand offering me comfort and
reassurance. In my strongest moments,
I absolutely knew He would take
care of me.

"People in my church were wonderful. They
prayed for me and with me. They stepped up
to the plate and took me to the doctor, ran
errands, cooked meals, babysat, and looked
in on me. They showed me daily what a
follower of Christ looks like."

Renee, 38

*Renee said it is now her duty to give to others
who are in pain. She learned the value of
unconditional love - even from relative strangers.*

"**It** is

one of the **blessings**
of **good** friends
that you can afford
to be **stupid** with them."

Ralph Waldo Emerson

 **I** was so angry

at God when I found out I was sick. I thought if there was a God, He couldn't be a very loving God if He allowed such suffering and pain. For the first time in my life, I questioned why we lived, why we suffered, why we loved, why we died. WHY? WHY? WHY? Nothing made any sense. I came to realize that's why it's called faith. Because it doesn't contain logic or sense.

"While I was healing, I bounced all over the map. Sometimes I believed in God. Sometimes I didn't. Sometimes I found comfort in my faith in God. Sometimes, I felt lost, empty, and even abandoned. Today, my issues of faith are still not resolved. I do accept that it's a belief in something beyond my understanding and that I'm on a journey. "

Ginger, 46

"It's not unusual for someone in crisis to question their faith. In fact, it's natural. Faith is not static. It is fluid, dynamic and vibrant. My job is to listen to their thoughts and let them come up with their own answers. I'm not doing my job if I tell them their lack of faith is wrong. It is often through doubt that we rise to a higher level of faith."

Vicki Finkstein
Chaplain

Many people go to talk to their church pastors, hospital chaplains, or local spiritual leaders when they are ill. They are not all the same so remember if you don't feel good sharing with this person, find someone else.

"For if you have **faith**,

even as small
as a tiny mustard seed
you could say
to this mountain,
"Move!"
and it would go far away.

Nothing
would be impossible."

Matthew 17:20

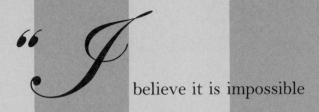

"*I* believe it is impossible

for someone to hear they have cancer and not question their mortality. We are brought face to face with the question of dying and what that means to us. I know I asked myself what was the meaning of my life and had I fulfilled it.

"I was given another chance to make sure I truly lived my life fully. For that I am truly grateful.

"I now laugh more, and work and play harder. I even have learned to let go of lots of really unimportant things."

Richard, 73

Richard wishes that he had done some of that introspection earlier in his life but accepts that it is through difficult times that many of us seek the meaning of life.

*M*any survivors said that their friends and neighbors were very helpful. Some of the things you can ask them to do are:

Come for a visit when you don't want to be alone, sometimes just sitting there without talking.

Drive you to and from appointments.

Give you a hug or hold your hand.

Make you or your family a sandwich or meal.

Rent a video or DVD and leave it or stay and watch it together.

Babysit your children or take them out for a special treat.

Remind you why you are fighting this disease.

Give you a massage, manicure, or haircut.

Let you vent your anger, frustrations, or fears about what is happening.

Give you another hug.

Remember that your friends and neighbors want to help!

"**Surround yourself**

with people who
respect
and
treat you well."

Claudia Black

 ven after

you finish all your treatments, you may find
that you will still experience chronic fatigue.
Your energy may not rebound for six months,
maybe even a year. Sometimes that's when
depression can set in. Patients feel like they
should be completely well and get frustrated
when they don't bounce back as fast as they
think they should.

"Give yourself a break. Continue to be gentle
with yourself and don't let anyone tell you
the fatigue isn't real."

Mary K. White, R.N.
Oncology Certified Nurse

"To everything

there is a
time and **purpose** under heaven;

A time to **be born;**
A time to **die;**
A time to **plant;**
A time to **sow;**
A time to **kill;**
A time to **heal;**
A time to **laugh;**
A time to **cry;**
A time for **keeping;**
A time for **throwing away;**
A time for **war;**
A time for **peace.**"

Ecclesiastes 3:1-8

"*L*earning to live with

a colostomy bag was difficult. It was tricky learning to change it, watch for leakages, and be aware of odors. I had to change my life style. I had to think about things like how long I would be gone when I was wearing the bag or needed to change it, what clothes I could wear so it wouldn't show or wear comfortably, what would happen if I had to undress or have sex. For a while, I felt humiliated but I learned to cope when I thought about the alternative of not continuing to live. Then wearing a colostomy bag seemed like a minor annoyance."

Joy, 60

For ten years, Joy has worn a colostomy bag and says she has adjusted well. She has given a lot of her time as a volunteer to others who are striving to live a healthful life following treatment for cancer.

"The storm

of the last night
has **crowned**
this morning
with
golden peace."

Tagore (from *Stray Birds*)

"*A*fter finishing treatment,

I then got to look forward to going back for regular check-ups. No, I don't think so.... Every time my check-up date was close, I found myself stewing about whether or not they would find cancer again. I was anxious and tense before each check-up. So far I have been able to leave my appointments with a great sense of reassurance that I was disease-free for another three or six months."

Robert, 73

If you're worried about going to your check-ups and what might come to light, you're not alone, says Robert. Just remind yourself that what you want is <u>another</u> clean bill of health. Then when you get it, let out a huge sigh of relief and celebrate!

"To have

reconstructive surgery or not-that was the question. I decided that I wanted to reconstruct my breast after a mastectomy. I felt pretty lucky because my husband said he truly didn't care. He still held me and touched me. However, what I found was that I did care. I was struggling with the way I looked when I saw myself naked. I finally accepted that maybe it was vanity but I didn't care. I wanted to look better. I decided to go through the surgery and I'm so glad I did. It made a world of difference in the way I felt about myself."

Jane, 46

At first, Jane believed that part of her decision was based on her age at the time she lost her breast. However, she says that she heard women of all ages express many of her thoughts and fears. Jane realized that wanting to have two breasts is important to many women.

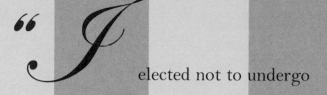

"*I* elected not to undergo reconstructive surgery after my mastectomy. I absolutely did not want to have more surgery. I have lived with prosthetics since then and I've adjusted rather nicely. With clothes on, no one can tell. And when I'm alone, I don't always bother to wear anything.

"It was an adjustment at first. I thought everyone was looking at my breasts. Maybe they were, but I finally got past that and decided I didn't care. I was happy with myself."

Mary, 69

Mary says we need to get past the belief that breasts make us women. In her opinion, women need to be thought of for their minds, hearts, and actions, not their breasts.

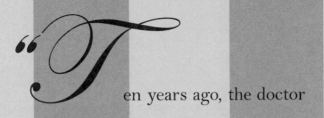

"Ten years ago, the doctor

found several tumors on my vocal chords. I had my voice box removed during the surgery that followed. I have lived with a tracheostomy tube in my throat since that time. I have learned to talk using a speech aid appliance. I now talk slower than before and my family tells me I use my hands more to communicate.

"Then, I was diagnosed with colon cancer and went through more surgery and treatments. Of course, I had more adjustments to make in my life. Here I am today, still living after surviving two major cancers."

Louis, 73

Don't give up, Louis says. He thought he was a "goner" for sure, when he was diagnosed with the second cancer. Six years later, he says he's still got more living to do.

'Somehow

we learn
who we **really** are

and then **live**
with the
decision."

Eleanor Roosevelt

"Many people

will need to make life style changes so they can remain healthy and active for the rest of their life. Certainly getting regular check-ups is at the top of the list.

"Some other changes include things like staying out of the sun and using sun blocks, especially for those with skin cancers. Other patients who have undergone radiation need to make sure they wear sunblock and protective clothing on the area which was exposed to radiation.

"Quitting smoking is important to prevent further damage. Adapting to various appliances like colostomy bags or tracheostomy tubes may take some adjustment.

"There may be times when you'll need oxygen because of changes in your lung capacity and you may have to adjust to carrying oxygen tanks or nebulizer treatments.

"Adjustment takes time. When you are struggling, concerned, or frustrated, we are here to help you. Please give us a call."

Mary K. White, R.N.
Oncology Certified Nurse

"Trying to balance

work, home and dealing with my illness was very stressful. I was tired from chemo, and I was worried. I had to work because I am a single mom with two kids, ages seven and nine. I had no choice. I couldn't take off three months. My kids didn't understand what was happening and things like taking a nap were impossible.

"I had a couple of friends who really pitched in and helped. One of them picked up my children at school and took care of them until 6 p.m., so I could come home and catch a quick nap. Another one helped me organize some meals so I could pop them in the oven and not have to deal with dinner decisions.

"I am grateful for their help. They saw me melt down from time to time and still stuck by my side. Don't hesitate to let your friends help. I think they know how much I truly appreciate them as a part of my life."

Donna, 38

"**My** boss wasn't very
tolerant of my illness. She said she
understood, but I'd see her rolling her
eyes or sighing heavily under her breath.
I felt guilty for taking time off but I
just plain didn't feel good."

John, 57

Some employers or colleagues will not under-stand what it's like to feel tired, rundown, and achy all over because of cancer treatments. John says it's important to let go of the guilt you might feel and remind yourself that they've never been through it and just plain don't understand.

125

"Be glad of life

because it gives you

the chance to **love**

and to **work**

and to **play**

and to **look at the stars.**

Henry Van Dyke

"About nine years ago,

I was diagnosed with a brain tumor and went through a variety of treatments including radiation and chemotherapy. Since that time, doctors have continued to find new and different tumors and I have pursued a myriad of treatments. The doctors have told me time and again, that my case is hopeless.

"Here I am: still alive-living with my wonderful husband, John, and surrounded by my loving family. In fact, I have defied the odds and spent the last year traveling, visiting with friends and family, and continuing to create wonderful times. I have done things I was told I would never do again. I attribute much of this to our trust, hope, and faith in God.

"Don't give up regardless of what anyone else tells you. Surround yourself with people who love you and whom you love. Believe in God's power. And don't buy into time limits. There is no such thing."

Jody, 33

Jody believes that the two most important attributes for being happy in life are the power of a positive attitude AND a strong faith in God. She has both.

**"Life is**

absolutely grand! I am so thrilled that I've got
another chance at life and I don't take it for
granted for one moment. I love my family, my
friends, my life. I even appreciate my work
more. Mostly, I just plain don't do things I don't
want to do any more. And I do more of the
things I do want to do.

"I hope I live another 50 years but I know that
regardless, I've lived these last eight more fully
than the previous 55.

"Thank God for life, for MY life!"

Mike, 63

*Mike suffered from a brain tumor many years ago
and after surgery and treatment, he said he relished
life like never before.*

 **"I've redefined**

the meaning of a quality life since I had cancer.
It's no longer chasing the almighty dollar,
desiring power, or working so long and so
hard. It's holding hands with my wife, fielding
unending questions from my grandchildren,
and golfing with my buddies."

Bob, 68

*Bob says he has another chance at life and he won't
blow it. He reminds us that on our deathbed, we
don't ask to go back to work. We ask for the people
we care about.*

any people

seek symbols of hope and courage as they proceed toward health and wellness.

Ribbons of various colors bind together those with similar circumstances. Listed below are the colors associated with different types of cancer:

Lavender/Purple: Cancer in general

Blue: Colo-rectal cancers

Teal: Ovarian/gynecological cancers

Clear: Lung cancers

Red: Multiple myeloma

Pink: Breast cancers

**This information was obtained
from the American Cancer Society**

*Hearts, angels and ribbons are available
through InnerSources, Inc.
1-800-366-9993*
www.goodmessages.com

My Story

*My favorite quotes, stories, and
personal recollections*

My own personal collection

of inspirational quotes and thoughts:

_____

_____

_____

_____

_____

_____

_____

_____

_____

_____

_____

_____

_____

_____

_____

_____

_____

_____

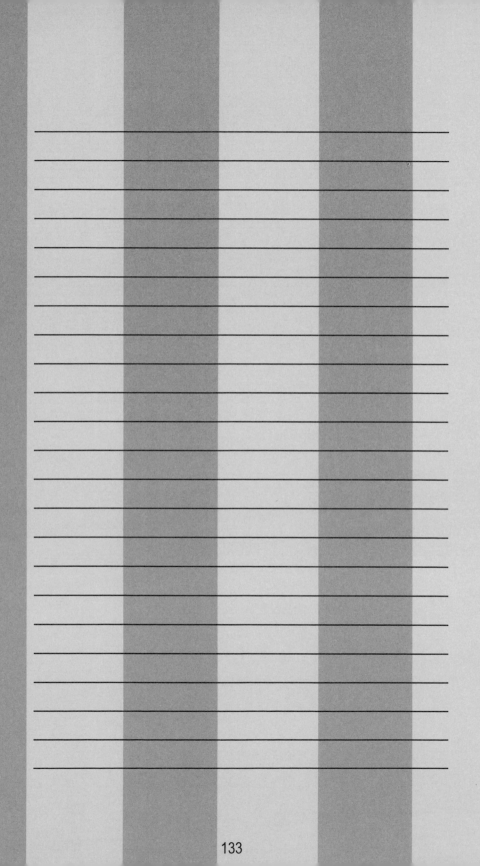

Ten Things

I want to do in this lifetime:

1. _____

2. _____

3. _____

4. _____

5. _____

6. _____

7. _____

8. _____

9. _____

10. _____

Ten Things

I Am Most Grateful for:

1. _____

2. _____

3. _____

4. _____

5. _____

6. _____

7. _____

8. _____

9. _____

10. _____

My Story

I was diagnosed with cancer:

_____
_____
_____
_____
_____
_____
_____
_____
_____
_____
_____
_____
_____
_____
_____
_____
_____
_____
_____
_____

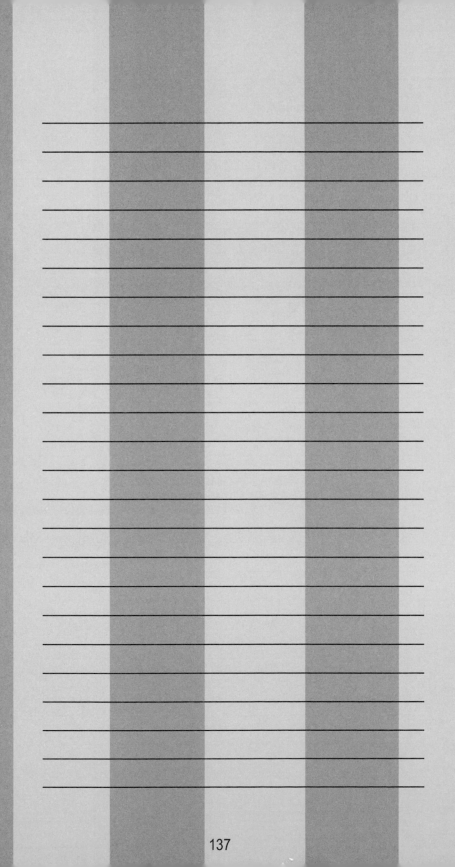

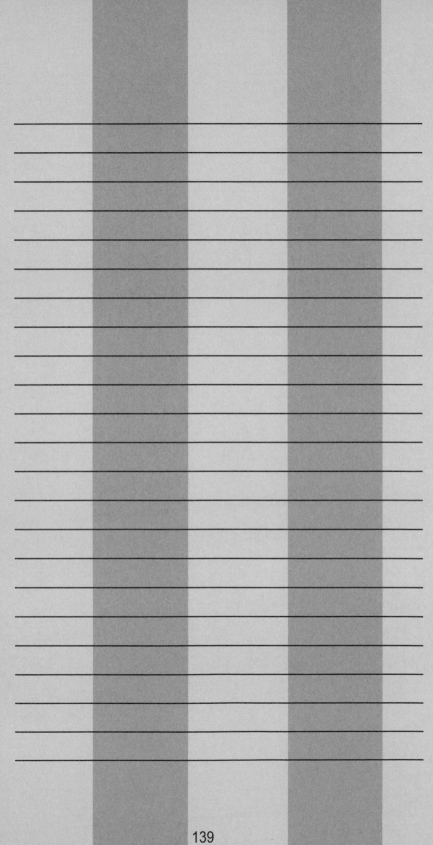